# M3 Half-tra

MW00862217

By Jim Mesko
Color by Don Greer
Illustrated by Joe Sewell

## in action

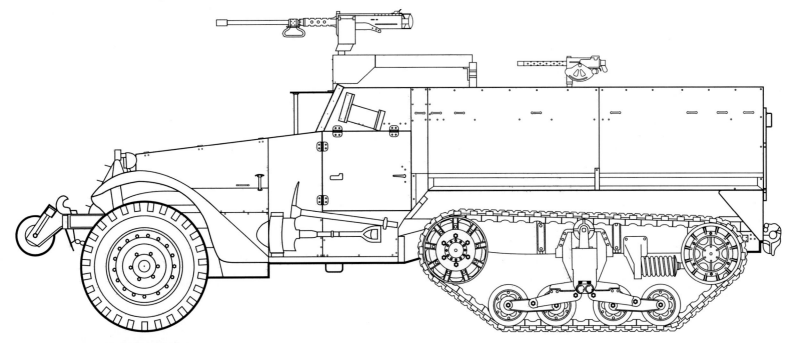

**Armor Number 34**

# squadron/signal publications

**AT EASE, an M3A1 of A Company, 17th Armored Engineer Battalion, 2nd Armored Division moves off the beach during the Normandy invasion in June of 1944.**

# Acknowledgements

PAM
U.S. Army
Richard Hunnicutt
ECPA
Mike Green

# Dedication:

To "Coach" Pearsons, for all he did on and off the field to help me to succeed. "THANKS COACH."

**COPYRIGHT 1996 SQUADRON/SIGNAL PUBLICATIONS, INC.**
1115 CROWLEY DRIVE  CARROLLTON, TEXAS 75011-5010

**ISBN 0-89747-363-9**

If you have any photographs of aircraft, armor, soldiers or ships of any nation, particularly wartime snapshots, why not share them with us and help make Squadron/Signal's books all the more interesting and complete in the future. Any photograph sent to us will be copied and the original returned. The donor will be fully credited for any photos used. Please send them to:

Squadron/Signal Publications, Inc.
1115 Crowley Drive
Carrollton, TX 75011-5010

Если у вас есть фотографии самолётов, вооружения, солдат или кораблей любой страны, особенно, снимки времён войны, поделитесь с нами и помогите сделать новые книги издательства Эскадрон/Сигнал ещё интереснее. Мы переснимем ваши фотографии и вернём оригиналы. Имена приславших снимки будут сопровождать все опубликованные фотографии. Пожалуйста, присылайте фотографии по адресу:

Squadron/Signal Publications, Inc.
1115 Crowley Drive
Carrollton, TX 75011-5010

軍用機、装甲車両、兵士、軍艦などの写真を所持しておられる方はいらっしゃいませんか？どの国のものでも結構です。作戦中に撮影されたものが特に良いのです。Squadron/Signal社の出版する刊行物において、このような写真は内容を一層充実し、興味深くすることができます。当方にお送り頂いた写真は、複写の後お返しいたします。出版物中に写真を使用した場合は、必ず提供者のお名前を明記させて頂きます。お写真は下記にご送付ください。

Squadron/Signal Publications, Inc.
1115 Crowley Drive
Carrollton, TX 75011-5010

**An M2A1 leads a column of trucks from the 331st Infantry Regiment, 83rd Infantry Division during operations with the 3rd Armored Division in the final stages of the "Battle of the Bulge." The M2 and M3 half-tracks provided much needed mobility for the infantry and their supporting arms and allowed them to keep pace with their tank counterparts. Throughout the war they would be used for a wide variety of jobs and proved to be a successful vehicle in nearly all the duties assigned. (Army)**

3

# Introduction

During the First World War, numerous new weapons were introduced which radically altered the face of war. One in particular, the tank, had the potential to revolutionize land warfare as it then existed. During the war, French and British tanks, although able to pierce the barbed wire entanglements and trenches which dominated the front, were not able to hold on to their gains due to a lack of infantry support. Eventually, the tanks were relegated to the role of infantry support, rather than allowed to strike out on their own. This became the accepted doctrine in the post-war years due to the conservative nature of most of the higher ranking generals in Britain, France and the United States. Germany, not allowed tanks under the terms of the Versailles Treaty, initially did nothing in this area since it had no tanks.

Fortunately, a few far sighted individuals in their countries tried to find ways to allow infantry to keep up with tanks and exploit their mobility. While the obvious solution would have been to convert tanks to carry infantry, cost mitigated against this approach. Trucks could carry infantry on good roads but were obviously unable to follow tanks across rugged terrain. But if the tracked features of a tank were mated with a truck body, this might offer a viable solution to the problem.

In the United States, interest in this type of vehicle had resulted in the purchase of two half-track vehicles manufactured by the French firm of Citroen-Kegresse in 1925 for testing by the Ordnance Department. Tested as prime movers at Aberdeen Proving Grounds for the 75MM artillery piece, the Army was impressed by the performance of the vehicles.

An additional vehicle was acquired during 1931 for further testing. Then, in 1932, an American firm, James Cunningham and Sons, completed a pilot version of their own, similar to the French vehicles under the designation Half-track Car T1. Thirty additional vehicles, T1E1s, were procured by the government, being identical to the T1, except for the body. A number of these were fitted with different suspensions, one being a volute spring type, with the vehicle being designated the T1E3. This type of suspension would eventually form the basis for the M2 and M3 Half-tracks. Work continued on the half-track variants using differ-ent truck bodies, suspensions, and tracks, but it was not until 1938, that the first armored version was developed.

This came about as a result of a need by the Cavalry for a vehicle better suited for cross-country movement than the current scout cars then in use. In addition, the new vehicle was also to be suitable for use as a prime mover. During 1938, a M3 Scout Car was fitted with a half-track suspension from the T9 Half-track truck. Designated the T7, this vehicle showed that such as configuration was possible, but also highlighted potential problems. The T7 was underpowered and lacked powered front wheel drive. In addition, its interior was cramped and lacked adequate internal stowage. The artillery branch looked at the T7 and submitted a request for a similar vehicle with a more powerful engine and front wheel drive. This new vehicle resembled the T7, but was designated the Half-track Scout Car T14. After field tests in the Summer of 1940, the Army decided to purchase the T14 for use as a prime mover and ammunition carrier with the revised designation, Half-track Car M2.

While the T14 was undergoing testing, infantry officers were present and in general liked what they saw. Since the German "Blitzkrieg" of Poland and Europe had emphasized the importance of mechanization of the Army's ground forces, a suitable vehicle was needed to meet the needs of the infantry component of the new mechanized Army then in the process of being organized. After reviewing the T14, a request was made for a similar vehicle with a lengthened body for use as a personnel carrier. This modified vehicle received the designation Half-track Personnel Carrier T8 and the Diamond T Motor Compamy received a contract to develop this model, which eventually became the Half-track Personnel Carrier M3.

Satisfied in general with both the T14 and T8, the Army began to lay plans for the creation of a modern ground force capable of taking on Hitler's vaunted Wehrmacht, despite the fact that the U.S. was officially still neutral. The swift, overwhelming victories which the Germany Army had achieved over Poland, Belgium, Holland and France were credited to the new Panzer divisions and the Luftwaffe. As a result, the U.S. began a rapid expansion of its own army, navy and air force against the day when the U.S. would probably be drawn into combat with Germany and its Axis partners, Japam and Italy.

With regard to the expansion of the Army, initial steps were taken to develop armored divi-

**Following the First World War the U.S. Army used a wide variety of armored cars such as this T7. Unfortunately, the inherent inability to negotiate rough or soft terrain made them unsuitable for operations except on roads or flat ground, which limited their overall usefulness. The T7 would eventually evolve into the M2 and M3 Scout Car. (PAM)**

**During the 1930s, the Army experimented with a number of half-track configurations to improve the mobility of trucks. An early vehicle was this T5 artillery prime mover which helped lay the groundwork for later vehicles such as the T9 Half-track truck. (PAM)**

sions, similar to what the Germans had used to defeat the Allies so quickly. This required the procurement of modern tanks and half-tracks to meet the firepower and mobility which the Panzer divisions had exhibited in their lightning victories.

As a result of this need for expansion, the Ordnance Department called a meeting in Washington of representatives of the three companies which had been involved in the initial bidding or development of the T14 and T8. These were the Autocar Motor Company which had received a contract for 425 M2s, the Diamond T Motor Company, which had developed the T8 from the T14 and the White Motor Company which been one of the low bidders for the initial contract. The Ordnance Department realized that the scope of expansion being planned ruled out the possibility that any one company could handle the manufacturing of the quantities of vehicles needed. So as to make logistics as simple as possible, the Army required that all vehicles which the three companies manufactured be alike, with all parts interchangeable expect for armor plating.

A Half-track Engineering Committee was formed from representatives of the three companies and the Ordnance Department to insure that this goal was achieved. As a result of these discussions, large scale production of the M2 Half-track Car and M3 Half-track Personnel Carrier was authorized in mid-October of 1940.

In 1938, an M3 Scout Car was fitted with a tracked suspension unit from the T9 and designated the T7. Underpowered, it was reviewed by the various Army branches, including the Artillery branch which submitted a request for a similar but more powerful vehicle. This resulted in the T14 which proved to be a much better vehicle and later became the M2 Half-track Car. (PAM)

The Infantry Branch also looked at the T14 while it was undergoing tests and decided that in, view of developments in Germany, they might be able to use a similar vehicle. They submitted a request for a similar vehicle like the T14, but with a longer body. This was initially designated the Half-track Personnel Carrier T8, but later went into production as the M3 Half-track Personnel Carrier. (PAM)

## Development

**M2 Half-track Car**

**M3 Half-track Personnel Carrier**

**M3 75ᴍᴍ GMC**

**M3 57ᴍᴍ GMC**

**T30 75ᴍᴍ HMC**

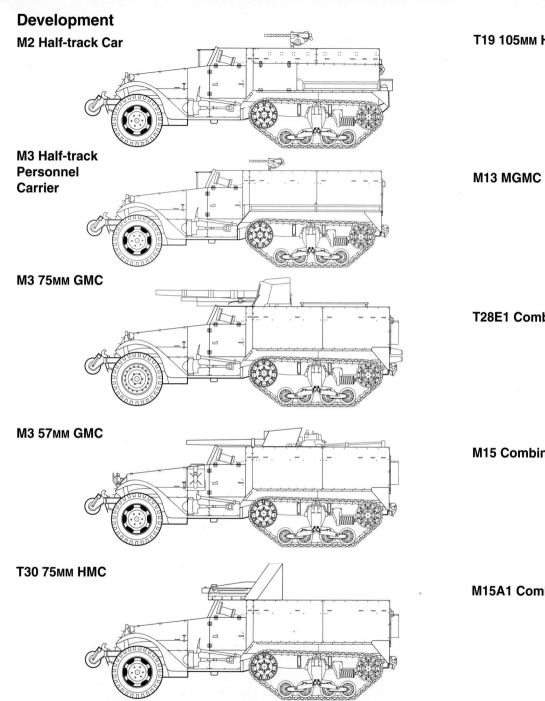

**T19 105ᴍᴍ HMC**

**M13 MGMC**

**T28E1 Combination GMC**

**M15 Combination GMC**

**M15A1 Combination GMC**

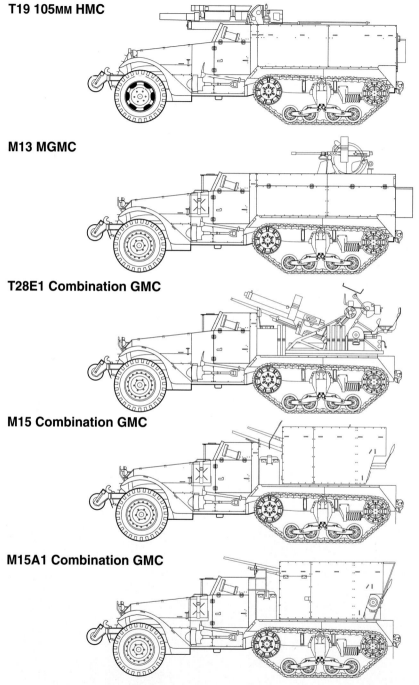

# M2 Half-track Car

The M2, which evolved out of the T14, was powered by a White 160AX engine which replaced the White 20A L-head engine used in the T14. It was chosen over three other types for its power and reliability. In order to simplify things, steering and shifting were similar to a commercial truck, with the driver being seated on the left with a five speed transmission, four forward and one reverse. Front wheel drive was through a Timken F35-HX-1, split type, hypoid spiral bevel unit with a ration of 6.8.1. The rear bogie suspension was a Timken 56410-BX-67 unit which utilized an endless rubber-band track. This was made of molded rubber over steel cabling and metal track guides. Even with the half-track assembly the M2 had a top speed of 45 mph on a paved surface, although off the road, this was substantially lowered.

The general layout of the M2 was similar to the M3A1 Scout Car. It had a normal capacity of ten men, with three seats in the front, and seven in the rear. The driver sat on the left, with a passenger seat to the extreme right. Another seat was between them and further back, which faced forward. Behind it was another seat that faced to the rear. On either side of these seats were large storage bins, located behind the two front seats. These were approximately in the center of the vehicle, and separated the front and rear parts of the body. Access to the storage compartments was through armored doors on the sides of the vehicle just behind the two front doors. The top of the bins were also hinged, allowing access to the top shelf. On either side of the rear compartment were three additional seats, which faced inward. Behind the rear two seats were the main fuel tanks, which each held thirty gallons of fuel. These were constructed of sheet steel and had a bullet sealing cover.

The main armament of the M2 was mounted on a skate rail which ran along the upper inside edge of the hull. While the "official" armament was one .30 caliber and one .50 caliber machine guns, mounted on tracks on the rail, a wide variety of armament arrangements was used by individual crews depending on their preference and what they could lay their hands on. In addition to the skate rail, there was also a pedestal mount for a machine gun on the left side of the rearward facing seat, next to the left storage bin.

Armor protection for the vehicle was made up of quarter inch thick armor plates which were bolted to the body framework with oval head screws and self locking nuts. The only exception to this was the windshield plate and the door shield plates which were half inch thick armor.

Access to the vehicle was either through the two doors for the drivers compartment or over the sides of the vehicle. Due to the skate rail there was no rear access door, since the rail blocked the use of such a door. The armored windshield plate was hinged and could be raised for increased visibility. When lowered, small vision ports were located for the driver and passenger with sliding armor plates which could be opened or closed as needed. The two side doors had a similar arrangement for the top of the door which was hinged and could be lowered toward the outside of the door when conditions warranted.

At the front of the vehicle, armored louvers could be lowered to protect the radiator and engine, or left open to increase the air flow for cooling purposes. On the bumper, an unditching roller was normally fitted, although this could be replaced with a winch for unditching or other uses.

Production of the M2 began in the Spring of 1941 and when production ceased during 1943, some 11,415 vehicles had come off the assembly line. White Motors and Autocar were the

**The M2 was powered by a White 160AX engine which developed 127 horse power. There was a five speed transmission with four forward and one reverse speed. While this vehicle is undergoing major engine work, for routine maintenance, normally the side flaps of the engine compartment folded up and over to allow access to the engine compartment. (PAM)**

**The M2 was similar in many respects to civilian trucks aside from its half-track configuration. This was to make it relatively simple to produce, since as many commercial type components as possible were to be used in its manufacture. In addition, this made the training of drivers and mechanics easier since many were familiar with such vehicles. This M2 was assigned to the Armored Force School at Fort Knox, Kentucky. (PAM)**

The M2 was provided with front wheel drive through a Timken F35-HX-1 split type hybrid spiral bevel unit. This allowed for better control and movement over rough or soft terrain, a feature missing on the German equivalent, the SdKfz 251, which did not perform as well in similar conditions. (PAM)

two companies involved in the manufacture of the M2, with the former producing 8,423 and the latter assembling 2,992.

Initially, the M2 was envisioned as an artillery prime mover and ammunition carrier. Since it carried only ten men, it was not large enough for the standard infantry squad and was not considered for use in this capacity. As armored infantry doctrines were developed, however, the M2 was used as a carrier for machine gun squads or in armored reconnaissance units until the new M8 Armored Car became available.

# M2A1 Half-track Car

The M2A1 came about as a result of complaints concerning the skate rail which had proven awkward to use under combat conditions. In order to solve this problem, the Ordnance Department developed the M2E6 prototype which replaced the skate rail with an M32 truck machine gun ring which was mounted above the passenger position of the drivers compartment. This led to the new M49 ring mount or "pulpit" arrangement which help eliminate the problems associated with the skate rail.

In addition, three pintle mounts were fitted on the sides and rear of the troop compartment for a .30 caliber machine gun to supplement the .50 caliber machine gun on the M49 mount.

Production of these improved M2A1s started in late 1943 and ceased during 1944 after 1,643 had been produced by White and Autocar. In addition, over 5,000 M2 were rebuilt as M2A1s with the new gun mount.

This stripped down M2 chassis shows the relative simplicity of the design. From the beginning the Army was concerned with keeping M2/M3 production as simple as possible and the design was tailored to this requirement. This allowed for the maximum utilization of the large American automotive manufacturing base which gave the U.S. and its allies a quantitative edge over the Axis powers. (PAM)

The rear suspension unit was a Tilden 56410-BX-67 model which drove an endless rubber band track. This track was formed by vulcanizing rubber over the steel framework and cables of the track. The four small wheels of the suspension, which the vehicle rode on, were able to pivot so that the vehicle could negotiate extremely rough terrain or steep slopes. In the extreme, the rear idler could literally be in contact with the ground when the bogies pivoted while climbing a steep slope.

While the M2 and M3 were very similar, there were two features which made for easy identification. The M2 had a shorter rear body and had storage bins behind the doors to the drivers compartment. (PAM)

## Development

**M2 Half-track Car**

Interior Skate Rail For Armament

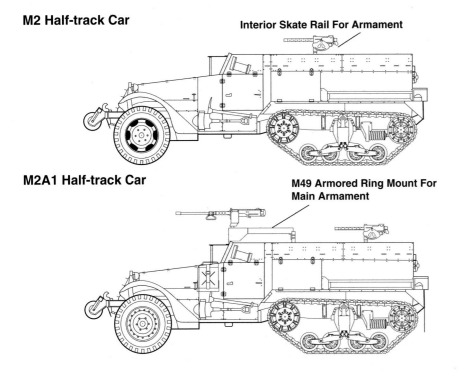

**M2A1 Half-track Car**

M49 Armored Ring Mount For Main Armament

From overhead the general seating arrangement and how the stowage boxes divided the drivers compartment from the rear troop section is revealed. The skate rail which ran around the entire compartment is very evident and made it impossible to fit a door to the rear wall for troops to exit. (PAM)

This M2 on display at Fort Knox has its stowage hatch open to show the interior shelves and ammunition cases stowed there. The "Pioneer Tool Rack" on the side was not normally fitted to the M2 since the tools in it were carried on other holders (it may have been mounted for publicity purposes). The tires are of the early type as are the hubcaps and headlights. On later models the headlights were able to be detached. The rack on the side is for mines, and is loaded with anti-tank mines. (PAM)

9

In addition to the new ring mount for a .50 caliber machine gun, provisions were also made for mounting three more machine guns, usually .30 caliber guns, on pintle mounts in the rear compartment. Also evident are the large side door which allowed access to the stowage bins and the mine rack loaded with anti-tank mines. The post behind the drivers compartment it a radio antenna mast. (Hunnicutt)

The awkward arrangement of the skate rail around the fighting compartment of the M2 led to the decision to delete it and place the main armament in an armored ring mount above the passengers side of the front compartment, under the designation M2A1. This mount allowed for a full 360 degree coverage without interfering with the troops in the rear. This particular vehicle also carries the newer detachable headlights and is fitted with a winch, which was not that common on the M2 series. (Hunnicutt)

Even with the elimination of the skate rail, there was no redesign of the rear wall to incorporate a door. This was one of the weaker points of the M2 under combat conditions as the troops either had to exit over the side or through the drivers compartment. The object on the rear of the vehicle is a tripod mount for a machine gun while the rods above it are for a tarp which could be fitted to cover the rear. The steps on either side of the rear were features of the M2 which made it easily distinguishable from the M3. (Hunnicuit)

The M2A1 could be fitted with a canvas cover for protection against the elements either for the troops or during storage or shipping. There are numerous tie downs which can be seen along the bottom of the canvas cover. Provisions were also made for the various protrusions, such as the main machine gun armament and radio antenna mast, which were standard on the vehicle. The M2 had a gas/water can fitting on either side of the vehicle just ahead of the drivers compartment doors. (Hunnicutt)

# M3 Half-track Personnel Carrier

The M3 was very similar in appearance to the M2, in fact the forward portion back to the drivers compartment was identical. The M3 was slightly longer than the M2 and lacked the stowage box doors behind the drivers compartment, since the boxes were not used on the M3 series. Internally, there was a major rearrangement. In the drivers compartment, the middle seat was moved forward to a position in line with the driver and passenger seats. The fuel tanks were relocated forward to the position formerly used by the stowage boxes and the middle rearward facing seat was deleted. In its place, a pedestal mount for a machine gun was added in the center of the floor. On either side, running in a row directly behind the driver and passenger seats, were five additional seats which faced inward. The last three seats had room for equipment behind their backs along with scabbards for rifles. Additional storage was also available under the seat cushions. Since the primary purpose of the M3 was as a personnel carrier, there was a rear door for exit or entry. As a result, the skate rail found on the M2 was deleted. Additional pintle mounts could be fitted to supplement the pedestal mount which could be fitted with either a .30 or .50 caliber machine gun.

To help over rough terrain, an unditching roller, as on the M2, was fitted to the front bumper. A winch could also be fitted in place of the roller to help the vehicle extract itself from mud or to help other vehicles. This unit was powered off the drive train.

Production of the M3, by White, Autocar and Diamond T, began during 1941 and continued until 1943. By that time, 12,499 vehicles had been produced, although some of these would be rebuilt as M3A1s.

While the M3 had been designed specifically for use as an armored personnel carrier for an infantry squad, it was quickly pressed into service for a wide variety of purposes. Like the M2, it was employed to carry ammunition for field artillery units, as a command vehicle, for ambulance work and as a maintenance vehicle. In addition, it also served as a basis for a number of specific modifications which received their own designations.

## M3A1

As in the case of the M2, the armament arrangement of the M3 was considered unsatisfactory. As a result of tests with the M2E6, which led to the M49 machine gun mount on the M2A1, the same modification was made to the M3, resulting in the M3A1. This model went into production in late 1943 and ended in 1944 with a total production run of 2,862 by White, Autocar and the Diamond T Company. In addition, a large number of M3s were upgraded to M3A1 standards through rebuilds and field modifications.

## M3A2

In an attempt to ease production, the Ordnance Department decided in early 1943, to consolidate the M2 and M3 into a single vehicle. The prototype, designated the T29, was ready for testing in the Spring of 1943, and was accepted for production in October under the designation M3A2. By that time, however, the need for half-tracks had declined and production of this variant did not start. The main difference between the M3A2 and M3A1 was the addition of an armored shield on the ring mount, movable storage boxes at the rear, and easy addition or removal of seats in the rear compartment.

## Development

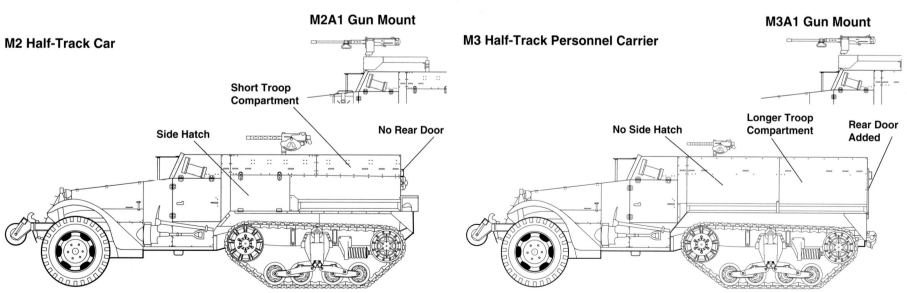

M2 Half-Track Car

M2A1 Gun Mount

Short Troop Compartment

Side Hatch

No Rear Door

M3 Half-Track Personnel Carrier

M3A1 Gun Mount

No Side Hatch

Longer Troop Compartment

Rear Door Added

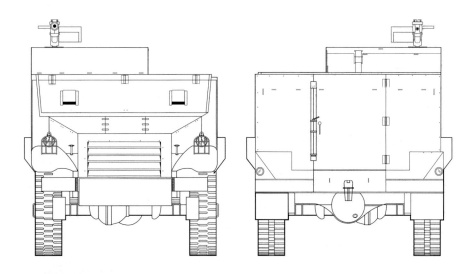

# Specification

## M3A1 Half-track

Width.......................7.29 feet (2.22 m)
Length.....................20.75 feet  (6.32 m)
Height.....................8.8 feet (2.69 m)
Empty Weight.........15,300 pounds (6,940 kg)
Maximum Weight... 20,500 pounds (9,298.8 kg)
Powerplant............  One 127 hp White 6 cylinder in line engine.
Armament...............One .50 caliber machine gun and provision for two .30 caliber machine guns..

Speed..................45 mph (72.4 km/h)
Range..................210 miles (337.9 km)
Crew...................13

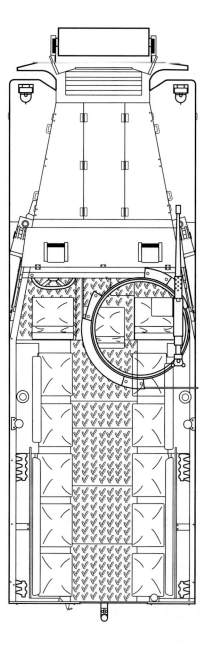

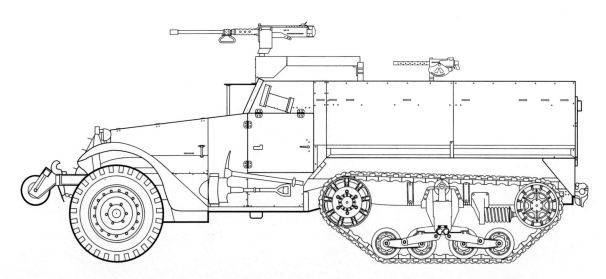

The main external differences between the M2 and the M3 was the longer rear compartment on the M3 and the lack of a storage bin behind the drivers compartment. This is a late M3 which has been fitted with dismountable headlights and late style wheel hubs. As reports filtered back from the field and from tests at bases like Fort Knox, improvements were made to the general design and retrofitted to earlier vehicles. (Hunnicutt)

The M3 was also fitted with a door at the rear which eased access to the troop compartment and allowed for a quicker and safer exit under combat conditions. This M3 has been fitted with the side mine rack which was introduced in August of 1942. In addition a non-standard stowage rack has been added to the side. (PAM)

From overhead the differences between the M2 and the M3 are clearly evident. The elimination the storage boxes allows easy access from front to rear and two extra seats. The fuel tanks have been moved forward in place of the storage boxes and the space behind the rear three sets of seats can be used for rifle stowage and extra gear. Additional space is also available under the seats which are mounted on folding panels. Directly between the first two seats is a pedestal mount for a machine gun. (PAM)

13

The pedestal machine gun mount was not particularly popular with M3 crews. The M3 could be fitted with either .30 (shown) or .50 caliber machine guns. The seats of this vehicle have been removed so that the storage bins under the seats can be seen. These bins held numerous items including rations, ammunition, and tools. (PAM)

Complaints from the North African fighting led to the development of the M49 ring mount for both the M2 and M3. This eliminated the awkward pedestal arrangement in the rear compartment and gave a better field of fire through a 360 degree arc. The addition of this feature to the M3 resulted in the M3A1, which began coming off the production line in October of 1943. (Hunnicutt)

The armored ring mount provided protection from the front and right side, but less to the left due to the need not to restrict entry into the rear compartment. To supplement the main gun position, pintle mounts, like those fitted to the M2A1, were mounted in the rear compartment for additional firepower. (Hunnicutt)

The right side of the ring mount extended back over the rear front of the back compartment, but only a small bracing of plate extended over the rear portion of it since little enemy fire was anticipated from this quarter, On the M3.and M3A1 the mine rack ran the entire length of the side. Having all these mines on the side of the vehicle must have caused some concern for the crew and troops when it came under fire. (Hunnicutt)

In January of 1943, plans were made to consolidate the M2 and M3 designs into the one model, the T29 which eventually evolved into the M3A2. While the basic design centered around the M3A1, the interior could be arranged according to mission requirements and could seat between five to twelve men. Additional storage boxes could also be mounted on the rear, if needed. (Hunnicutt)

While the M3A2 was very similar to the M3A1 a close look at the armored ring-mount will reveal how the left side of the armor has been extended back even further then on the M3A1. Scaling ladders were also added to the sides. Although the M3A2 would have simplified production, by the time it was ready for introduction the half-track program had been cut back significantly and production was canceled. (PAM)

# M9 Half-Track Car and M5 Half-track Personnel Carrier

With the direct American involvement in the Second World War, after the attack on Pearl Harbor, the government realized that the U.S. would become the true "Arsenal of Democracy." In order to supply the Allies with the needed equipment, more manufactures were sought to broaden the base for the production of military equipment. Since the new quantities of half-tracks could not be fulfilled by the original three companies, the International Harvester Company was approached to help in the production of the vehicles. Unfortunately, certain changes had to be made in the earlier requirement for standardization of components. The major change was the substitution of homogenous armor plating in place of the face hardened steel used in the M2/M3 series. This was 5/16 inch thick compared to the quarter inch thick armor used on the earlier series and had less ballistic protection and weighed more than the face hardened plate.

In addition, certain International Harvester components were used, including the engines, front axle and transfer case in place of the original components. The two variants were designated M2E5 and M3E2 and when they were approved for production, they became the M9 Half-track Car and M5 Half-track Personnel Carrier.

There were certain outward differences between the M9 and M5 compared to the M2 and M3. The M9 was the same length as the M5 and M3 and did not have the outer access doors on the side of the vehicle for the storage bins. Both the M5 and M9 had flat fenders, rather than the rounded automotive style fenders used on the M2 and M3. At the rear, the corners were rounded rather than squared off, and unlike the M2, the M9 had a rear access door. Externally, both the M5 and M9 were almost identical and the only way to tell them apart was to look at the interiors.

As with both the M2 and M3, the M9 and M5 were updated with the M49 pulpit type machine gun mount, becoming respectively the M9A1 and M5A1. Due to the differences in components with this series compared to the M2 and M3, the bulk of these vehicles were shipped overseas under Lend-Lease. International Harvester produced a total of 11,017 vehicles between 1942 and 1944 with production being broken down as follows: M9 (2,026), M9A1 (1,407), M5 (4,625) and M5A1 (2,959).

## M5A2

During 1943, the Ordnance Department decided to eliminate the two production models and consolidate them into a single vehicle to ease production. The trial vehicle was designated the T31 and when accepted was redesignated the M5A2. By the time the vehicle was ready, however, a reduction in the total number of half-tracks needed led to the cancellation of the project.

### Half-Track Armament

**Browning M2 .50 Caliber Air-Cooled Machine Gun**

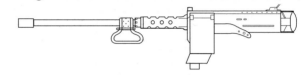

**.30 Caliber Air-Cooled Machine Gun**

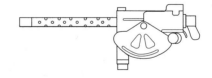

**.30 Caliber Air-Cooled Machine Gun**

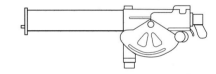

**M9A1 Half-track Personnel Carrier**

**M3A1 Half-track Personnel Carrier**

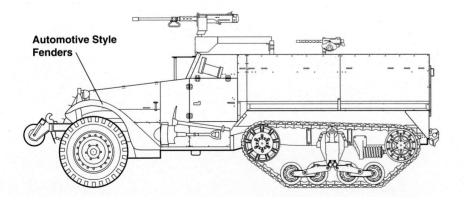

Automotive Style Fenders

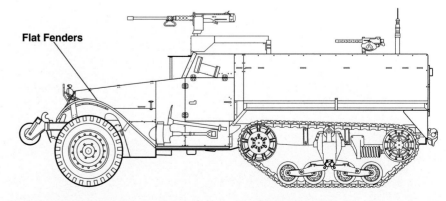

Flat Fenders

The M9 and M5 were variants of the M2/M3 produced by International Harvester to meet the growing need for vehicles after the U. S. entry into the war. There were a number of differences between these and the earlier models. Unlike the M2, the M9 did not have outer storage bin doors and the body length was the same as the M3/M5. The armor plate was 5/16 inch homogenous rather then face hardened, which made them heavier. The most noticeable external difference was the flat front fenders and rounded rear comers of the troop compartment. In addition, the M9 had a rear access door, unlike the M2. (PAM)

As with the earlier M3A1 vehicles, the armament varied depending on the crew. There were pintle mounts along the sides for additional machine guns to bolster the main .50 caliber machine gun armament. (PAM)

Like the M2 and M3 half-tracks the M9 and M5 were updated and designated M9A1 and M5A1 respectively when they were fitted with the M49 armored machine gun ring-mount. Externally, there was little difference between the two models although normally the M9 variants had the front mounted roller, while the M5 versions often carried a winch on the bumper. (PAM)

The lack of side access doors to the storage bins is obvious from the side on an M9A1. With the addition of the M49 .50 caliber machine gun ring-mount provisions were made for extra pintle mounts in the rear compartment. The two large upright posts are radio antenna masts. (Hunnicutt)

A general comparison of the two International Harvester vehicles reveals just how close the two vehicles were in their general outline. This M5A1 differs from the M9A1 (left) only in the addition of a roller on the front bumper in place of the winch installed on the M9A1. This vehicle has six rifles and four carbines stowed in the side racks in the rear compartment. (Hunnicutt)

Unlike its earlier counterpart, the M2, the M9 model did have a rear entry/exit door. The rounded rear corners of the troop compartment are very evident from the rear. As was usual, the mine rack is loaded with anti-tank mines. (Hunnicutt)

As the war progressed it was decided to combine the two International Harvester models into one design to ease production, as was done with the M2 and M3. Initially designated T31, the new model was redesignated the M5A2, but cutbacks in half-track production as the war entered its final phase led to a cancellation of the project and none were actually produced. (PAM)

# M4/M4A1 MMC

In October of 1941, an M2 was modified to carry a 81MM mortar in the rear compartment. This modification resulted in the M4 Mortar Motor Carriage (MMC) and the vehicle was assigned to the headquarters company of armored infantry and tank battalions. The modifications included removal of four seats in the rear, the addition of ammunition racks for the mortar and storage provisions for it. The mortar faced rearward and was not traversable. It was to be dismounted and fired from the ground, although in an emergency it could be fired from the vehicle. This arrangement was not particularly liked by the crews and some vehicles had the mortar reversed to fire forward despite official policy.

As the M4 was being produced, plans were being made, in late 1942, to mount the mortar on the M3. But, as the project was nor yet ready, it was decided to use the M2A1 to keep up with the anticipated needs. In order to allow the crews to fire the mortar from the half-track, the floor and mortar mounts were reinforced. These vehicles received the designation M4A1. They were distinguishable from the M4 by the large storage boxes mounted on the rear armor plate.

# M21 MMC

Dissatisfaction with the M4 led the Ordnance Department to mount the 81MM mortar on the M3. To alleviate the problems found in the M4, the floor and mortar mount were beefed up so that the mortar could be fired from the vehicle. In addition, it was positioned to fire over the front of the vehicle and could be traversed 30 degrees to either side. A pedestal mount was also provided for a .50 caliber machine gun in the rear. The prototype, designated the T19, was standardized in July of 1943 as the M21 MMC.

Production of the three vehicles ran from 1942 through 1944 with White Motor Company being the sole manufacture. In 1942, 572 M4s were produced, but this version was superseded by the M4A1, of which 600 were manufactured during 1943. In 1944, production of the M21 was begun, but due to a lessening need for mortar carriers, only 110 of these were produced.

**The interior layout of the M4 was very similar to the M2 aside from the mortar mount and ammunition racks in the rear. The mortar limited the effective traverse of the machine gun at the rear, as did the ammunition racks along the sides, a condition not desirable under combat conditions. (PAM)**

**Unlike the M2, the M4 had a small door at the rear to facilitate crew entry, ammunition restock and removal of the mortar for ground use. The M4 was designed for the mortar to be dismounted but crews often fired it from the vehicle. Some units even modified the mortar to a forward firing configuration. (Hunnicutt)**

# T21/T21E1

This variant of the M3 was similar to the M4 and M4A1, but instead mounted a 4.2 inch mortar. Work started on it in December of 1942, but used the M3 instead of the M2 as its base vehicle.

At first the mortar was fixed like the M4 to fire to the rear and received the designation T21. But, as the M21 had been modified to fire forward, it was decided to change to this arrangement, resulting in the T21E1. Due to the lessening requirement for half-track carriers and an increased interest in fully tracked vehicles, the project was terminated.

**The M4 was the first model of the M2 to be standardized as a production variant. It was fitted with a rearward firing 81MM mortar and could carry 126 rounds of ammunition. (Hunnicutt)**

The rearward firing mortar was not well liked by its crews in combat and when plans were made to mount the mortar on the M3 chassis, it was decided to reposition it so that it would fire over the front of the vehicle. These models were designated the M21 MMC. The longer rear body provided more room for the crew and eased the crowded conditions which existed in the M4 and M4A1 to a certain degree. (Hunnicutt)

There was an attempt to mount the 4.2 inch mortar in the M3 under the designation T21. Initially it was mounted to fire rearward as in the M4, but this was later revised and it was repositioned to fire forward, as in the M21. Interest in this configuration, the T21E1, was not sufficient and both variants were dropped in favor of fully tracked vehicles. (PAM)

In order to improve the ability of the M4 to function in combat the chassis was reinforced so the 81MM mortar could be fired from inside the vehicle without over-stressing the chassis. These models were designated the M4A1 and could be distinguished from the earlier M4 by the additional storage boxes mounted on the rear. (PAM)

Since the M3 did not have a skate rail and the mortar was positioned toward the front of the vehicle, the M21 had a pedestal mount in the rear for a .50 caliber machine gun, which was used for both air and ground defense. Production of the M21 started in January of 1944, but since there were enough of the M4 variants to meet Army requirements only 110 were produced before production was terminated. (Hunnicutt)

# M3 75MM Gun Motor Carriage

With the outstanding success of the German tank forces early in the war, the Ordnance Department looked for ways to improve the Army's anti-tank capabilities. In part, this resulted in the creation of the tank destroyer force, whose objective was to engage enemy armor. Unfortunately, there were no vehicles then in production which could do the job and ways were sought to correct this situation until specific vehicles were available for the force. One such stop-gap measure was the mating of the M1897A 75MM field gun, an American derivative of the famous French 75MM cannon of the First World War to the chassis of the M3. This conversion, initially designated the T12, had the gun welded to a box behind the drivers compartment. Nineteen rounds of ammunition were stored in racks under the gun mount with an additional forty rounds being stored in floor bins. The fuel tanks were moved to the rear in order to allow the gun room to traverse. It could move from 19 degrees to the left and 21 degrees to the right and could be elevated from -10 degrees through 29 degrees. The effective range of the 75MM anti-tank ammunition was approximately 1,000 yards and it could also be used to fire smoke and high explosive rounds.

On the T12, the only protection offered the gun crew was the flat shield from the gun. After field tests, the vehicle was rushed into production under the designation M3 75MM Gun Motor

Carriage (GMC). Initial vehicles were still fitted with the flat gun shield, but combat reports from the Philippines, where a large number had been sent, highlighted the lack of crew protection and in early 1942, a new box shield was designed which gave much better protection.

Despite its rather hurried development as a stop-gap weapon, the M3 75MM GMC was produced in fairly large numbers. Since the stock of M3A3 gun carriages was eventually depleted, older M2A2 models were substituted. These vehicles were designated 75MM GMC M3A1 and aside from the differences in the gun carriage, were identical to the earlier models.

This was the first significant variant of the basic M3 Half-track to be produced, with eighty-six being manufactured during 1941, followed by 1,350 in 1942 and ending with 766 during 1943, for a total production run of 2,202, the second most produced variant of the M2/M3 family. Later a significant number of vehicles were converted to standard half-tracks as the need for them diminished with the arrival of purpose built tank destroyers such as the M10 and M18.

**The M3 75MM GMC was the first major variant of the M3 series to go into production. It resulted from the need for a mobile tank destroyer following the stunning German victories in the opening days of the Second World War. It was basically a M3 mounting a M1897 75MM field gun. The initial version was designated the T12 and featured a flat gun shield. The front armor plate on the windshield was hinged to fold downward and had a notch for the bottom of the gun. (U.S. Army)**

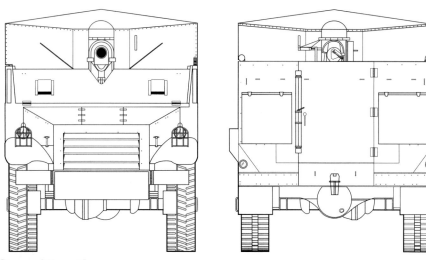

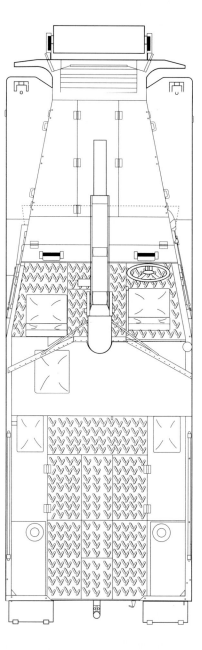

## Specification

### M3 75ᴍᴍ Gun Motor Carriage

**Width**........................7.29 feet (2.22 m**)**

**Length**.....................20.75 feet  (6.32 m**)**

**Height**......................7.75 feet (2.36 m)

**Empty Weight**........20,000 pounds (9,072 kg)

**Powerplant**............  One 127 hp White 6 cylinder in line engine.

**Armament**...............One 75ᴍᴍ cannon and provision for one .50 caliber machine gun.

**Speed**..................45 mph (72.4 km/h)

**Range**..................210 miles (337.9 km)

 **Crew**..................5

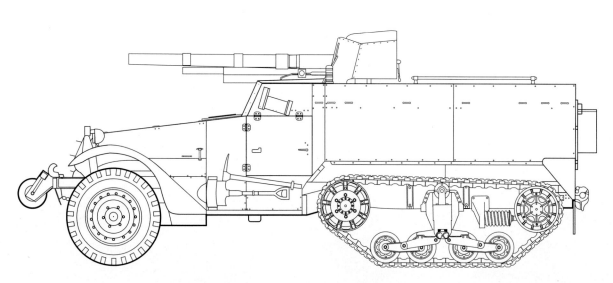

The conversion was relatively simple with the gun mount being welded to a metal frame which was bolted to the half-track body right behind the drivers compartment. Provisions were made for nineteen ready rounds of ammunition under the gun mount with additional rounds being stored in bins on the floor behind the gun. The wheels to the left are for elevation and traverse. (PAM)

The early gun shield on the original T12 and early M3 GMC provided little protection for the gun crews and led to various attempts to improve their protection, such as the shield shown here. This was a fixed shield which was bolted down to the top of the half track. (PAM)

This M3 GMC has been fitted with an indirect sighting system. Ironically, after the fighting in North Africa the M3 GMC was used mainly for indirect fire support during the fighting in Italy, although the Marines used the vehicle in their special weapons companies for anti-tank, direct, and indirect fire support. (PAM)

Eventually a partially enclosed gun shield with limited overhead cover was introduced on the M3 GMC which moved with the gun as it was traversed. This shield was introduced during early 1942 and first saw action during the fighting in North Africa. The post under the gun barrel is the travel lock, used to secure the gun while moving from place to place. (PAM)

# T48 57MM Gun Motor Carriage

Shortly after production of the M3 75MM GMC began, development started, in April of 1942, at Aberdeen Proving Grounds on another half-track tank destroyer using the British 6 pounder anti-tank gun. The vehicle was, however, fitted with the American version of this weapon, the 57MM M1 Gun. This half-track, designated the T48 57MM Gun Motor Carriage, was intended primarily for British use since the U.S. was planning on using the new M10 in its tank destroyer force to replace the M3 75MM GMC.

The T48 consisted of the M1 gun mounted right behind the drivers compartment with ammunition storage and other equipment located in the rear of the vehicle. In addition, the fuel tanks were moved to the rear of the vehicle. Due to the experiences with the gun shield on the early T12, the decision was made to fit the gun with an adequate shield from the start and a large box type shield with overhead protection was fitted to the gun. The M1 was able to traverse 27.5 degrees to either side and could be elevated from -5 degrees through 15 degrees.

Production of the vehicle began in December of 1942 and continued into 1943. The Diamond T Company manufactured a total of 962 of these vehicles, of which 680 were shipped to the British, while the remainder were retained in the U.S. and converted to M3A1 half-tracks. The British kept only a small number of their vehicles, which were also converted back to the half-track configuration. Most of the vehicles received were sent to the Soviet Union under Lend-Lease where they were used in their intended role in special independent tank destroyer brigades. Some were eventually supplied to Polish units serving with the Red Army in the latter part of the war.

Although the T48 went into production, by the time the vehicle was ready, the British no longer had a need for it and the bulk of the production run was supplied to the Soviet Union under Lend-Lease. Like the M3 GMC, the T48 was fitted with a downward folding armored windshield which had a notch in it for the gun. (PAM)

**The T48 was the result of a request by the British for a tank-destroyer equipped with a six pounder anti-tank gun. This model was armed with the American version of the gun, the M1 57MM gun. As with the M3 GMC, this version had the gun mounted directly behind the drivers compartment. Lessons from the M3 GMC shield situation led to the development of a suitable gun shield which provided adequate crew protection. Ammunition for the gun was stored in bins at the back and floor of the vehicle. (PAM)**

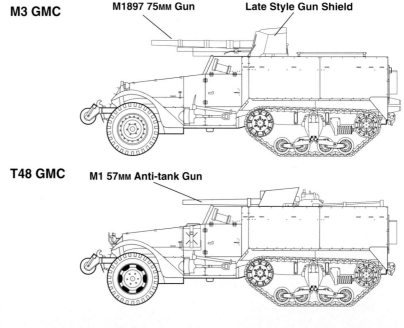

M3 GMC — M1897 75MM Gun — Late Style Gun Shield

T48 GMC — M1 57MM Anti-tank Gun

24

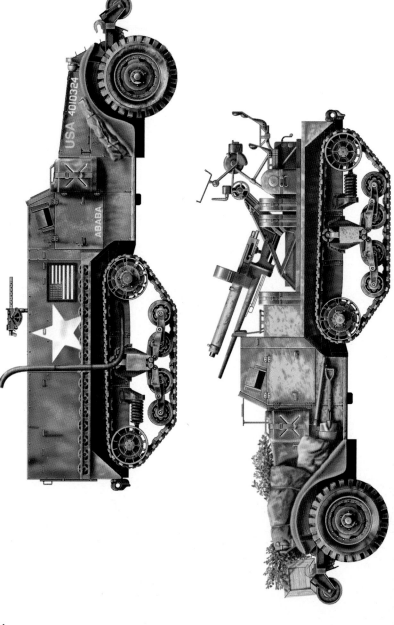

This M3 Half-track took part in Operation Torch, the invasion of North Africa during November of 1942.

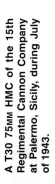

Camouflaged with foliage, this T28E1 Combination Gun Motor Carriage fought in Tunisia during 1943.

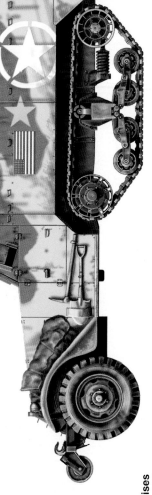

A T30 75мм HMC of the 15th Regimental Cannon Company at Palermo, Sicily, during July of 1943.

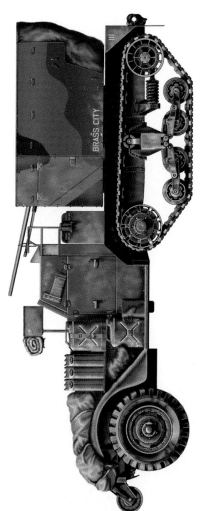

A M15A1 during pre-D-Day exercises in England during the Spring of 1944.

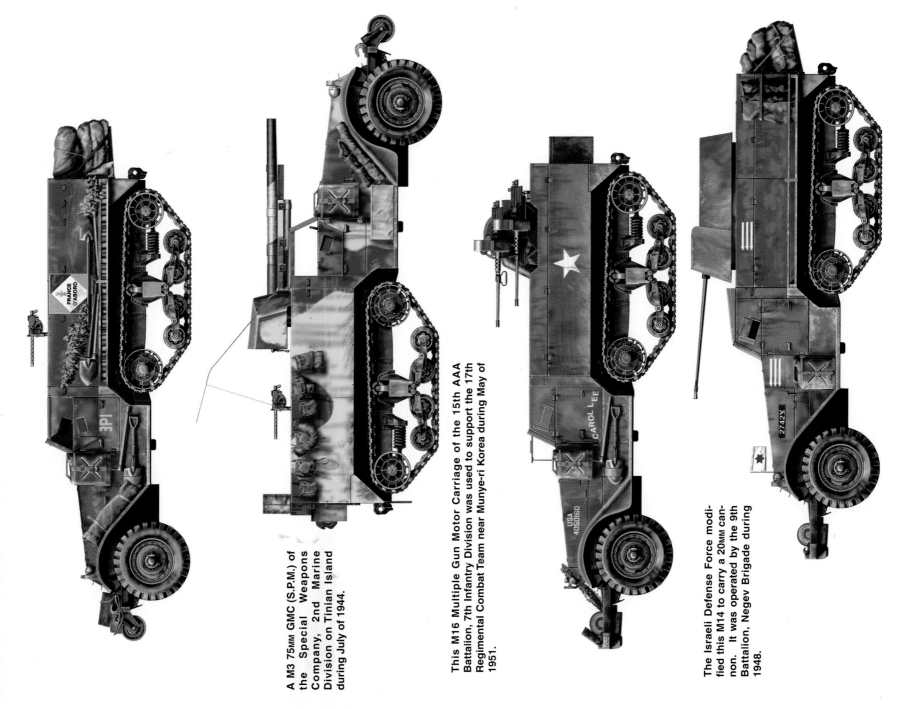

A M9 Half-track of the 5th Division Blindee, French Foreign Legion, in France during the Summer of 1944.

A M3 75MM GMC (S.P.M.) of the Special Weapons Company, 2nd Marine Division on Tinian Island during July of 1944.

This M16 Multiple Gun Motor Carriage of the 15th AAA Battalion, 7th Infantry Division was used to support the 17th Regimental Combat Team near Munye-ri Korea during May of 1951.

The Israeli Defense Force modified this M14 to carry a 20MM cannon. It was operated by the 9th Battalion, Negev Brigade during 1948.

# T30 75MM Howitzer Motor Carriage

To provide mobile support for the new armored forces, the Ordnance Department ordered the development, during late 1941, of an M3 equipped with a M1A1 75MM howitzer. This was only to be a stop-gap weapon until a more modern vehicle could be developed as a replacement. Two pilot models were produced during early 1942. These had the 75MM howitzer mounted in a similar arrangement to that used in the M3 75MM GMC. As on the M3 and the T48, the fuel tanks were repositioned to the back of the vehicle. The pilots and early production vehicles did not have a gun shield, but when reports came back from the Philippines about the M3 75MM GMC shields, it was decided to fit the T30 with one. A number of different types were tired, but eventually a high box like arrangement became standard. Due to this shield, the howitzer could be elevated to 50 degrees for indirect fire while it could traverse 22.5 degrees to either side. The White Motor Car Company produced 500 of the T30s, which were never redesignated, during 1942, although the last run of 188 vehicles were converted back to the M3 half-track configuration, before being issued to the troops.

**In order to provide an assault gun to equip the fledgling armored force it was decided to design an interim vehicle until one could be purpose desiged to fulfill the requirements laid down. This resulted in the T30, which had a M1A1 75MM howitzer mounted very similarly to the mounting used on the M3 75MM GMC. Initially, the weapon carried no sheild for the protection of the crew. (PAM)**

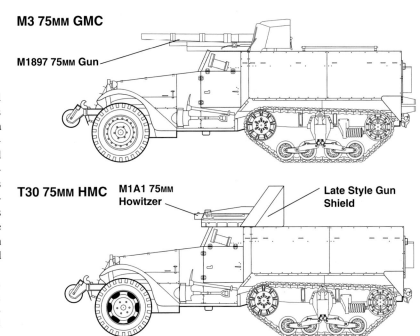

M3 75MM GMC

M1897 75MM Gun

T30 75MM HMC — M1A1 75MM Howitzer — Late Style Gun Shield

U.S.A. 4018410

In order to provide for gun crew protection it was decided to include a gun shield, as has been the case with the earlier M3 GMC and T48. Several different models of shield were tried until a rather high, boxy arrangement was finally chosen as the production standard. (PAM)

Like the M3 GMC, the howitzer was mounted directly behind the drivers compartment. Provisions were made for a pedestal mounted .50 caliber machine gun at the rear of the vehicle for anti-aircraft and ground defense. This vehicle is at the Armored Force School at Fort Knox. (PAM)

As with the M3 GMC, the fuel tanks were relocated to the rear of the T30 to make it easier to use the howitzer. Ammunition storage was in floor bins and in racks along the sides of the vehicle. (PAM)

This shield provided the crew with fairly good front quarter protection due to its high configuration, but the penalty for this was that the T30 was very conspicuous on the battlefield and hard to conceal. (PAM)

The main reason for using this shield was to allow the howitzer to be able to fire at a high angle so that it could be used in the indirect fire support role. The howitzer could be elevated to an angle of fifty degrees. (PAM)

Although the T30 was only meant as an interim weapon the lack of a successor led to it being deployed, not only in North Africa, but also in Sicily and Italy until finally replaced by the M8 75mm HMC which used the M5 light tank chassis. (PAM)

31

# T19 105mm Howitzer Motor Carriage

In conjunction with the T30 project, a requirement was also handed down for a half-track armed with a 105mm cannon. This was the largest weapon to be mounted on the M3 and there was some very serious concerns that the chassis would not be able to carry the weight. In order to hedge against this, a parallel development of a vehicle fitted with a 105mm pack howitzer was also started, the two vehicles being designated the T19 and T38 respectively. Eventually, the relative success of the T19 resulted in the cancellation of T38 development.

As with the M3 75mm GMC and T30, the cannon was mounted directly behind the drivers compartment with the fuel tanks being moved to the rear of the vehicle. The weapon itself was the M2A1 105mm howitzer, which had a maximum range of 1,700 yards. It could be traversed 20 degrees to either side and elevated from -5 degrees through 35 degrees. Shields were fitted on some vehicles, while others had none. A wide variety of ordnance could be fired including High Explosive, HEAT, White Phosphorus and chemical smoke.

The T19 was one of the least produced variants of the M3, with only 324 being manufactured by the Diamond T Motor Company during early 1942. This was due to the introduction of the M7 Priest armed with the same weapon in a modified M4 Sherman hull, which had greater mobility, protection and reliability. It could also fire while on the move, which was not recommended for the T19. The T19 probably stretched the limits of the M3 chassis to the maximum and its is surprising that the vehicle was able to function as well as it did with the heavy weight of the howitzer.

**The T19 was developed in conjunction with the T30 HMC project and mated an M2A1 105mm howitzer to the M3 half-track. At first it was thought that the M3 might not be able to bear the weight and recoil, but this proved not to be the case. (PAM)**

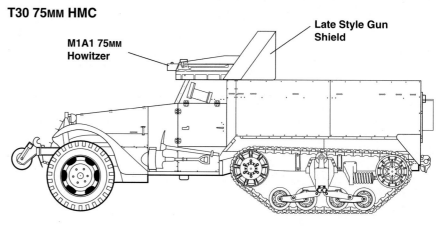

**T30 75mm HMC**

M1A1 75mm Howitzer

Late Style Gun Shield

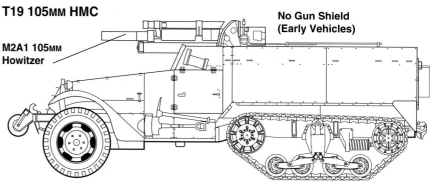

**T19 105mm HMC**

M2A1 105mm Howitzer

No Gun Shield (Early Vehicles)

Even though the conversion worked out, it stretched the M3 chassis to the limit and only 324 were produced before the design was replaced by the M7 Priest. The howitzer was basically bolted down to a box structure similar to the ones used on the other motor carriage conversions. The entire windshield and armor plate structure could be folded down to allow better movement of the howitzer. (PAM)

While the M3 could carry the weight and recoil of the 105MM howitzer the crew was extremely cramped in the rear when serving the weapon. There was little room to spare and if a ready supply of ammunition was kept in the back it became even more cramped. Earlier models were not fitted with shields, but later production vehicles had the standard howitzer shield attached. (PAM)

As with other such conversions the fuel tanks were moved to the rear and a pedestal mount was provided for a .50 caliber machine gun at the rear. The size of the howitzer and the room it took up is obvious from overhead. (PAM)

The howitzer had a twenty degree traverse left and right and could be elevated from minus five through fifty degrees. The rear door proved extremely helpful in replenishing ammunition or for removal of spent brass. Unlike the other conversions which could fire while on the move it was recommended that this not be done with the T19. (PAM)

# Combination Gun Motor Carriage T28E1, M15 and M15A1

While the M13/M16 family of anti-aircraft vehicles was under development, work was also started on an anti-aircraft vehicle using a 37MM cannon as its main armament. Designated the T28, it was fitted on the M2. While the cannon was the primary weapon, there were also twin .50 caliber machine guns mounted on either side of it which would be used to locate the target with tracer ammunition, at which time, the cannon would be fired.

Anti-aircraft weapons development, however, was at that time under the control of the Coast Artillery, which favored machine gun armament. As a result, four .50 caliber machine guns were substituted in the mount for the cannon/machine gun arrangement under the designation T37, leading to the cancellation of the T28 in the Spring of 1942.

In June of that year, however, the Armored Force requested a new vehicle to provide mobile protection for its forces in the upcoming invasion of North Africa scheduled for November of 1942. The canceled T28 was looked at and the decision was made to mount it on the M3 instead of the M2 due to the M3's longer chassis. With the invasion so close, work had to be expedited to get the vehicle, now designated the T28E1 Combination Gun Motor Carriage, into the hands of the invasion troops, but this was achieved with little time to spare. Eventually, eighty vehicles were manufactured by Autocar.

The unit itself consisted of an M1A1 37MM Automatic Anti-aircraft Cannon with two M2 .50 caliber machine guns positioned slightly above and on either side of the cannon. This was mounted on the back of the M3 and could revolve 360 degrees. Due to its size, the sides and rear wall of the M3 were completely removed. The guns could be elevated from -5 through 85 degrees, and they could be fired while on the move. There were no shields fitted to the mount, leaving the gun crew totally exposed.

The success of the T28E1 in North Africa, led the Army to decide to put it in full production during early 1943 under the designation M15. One of the few changes made to the original design was to add a turret like shield around the gun mount. The water-cooled .50 caliber machine guns were also replaced with air-cooled weapons and additional storage was added. These changes caused the weight to go up, with a resulting decrease in reliability and mobility. To help solve this, the M15 was modified to improve performance. A newer gun mount, the M3A1, replaced the original M42 mount with the machine guns being repositioned under the cannon. New sights and a slightly modified shield, which was lower and roomer, led to the M15A1, which became the main production version.

Besides the eighty T28E1s manufactured, Autocar produced 680 M15s during 1943 and 1,652 M15A1s during 1943 and 1944. All but 100 of these were used by U.S. forces. The 100 other vehicles were supplied to the Soviet Union under Lend-Lease.

The development of the T28 began in the Fall of 1941, but, due to the opposition of the Coast Artillery, it was canceled in favor of a machine gun armed system. It was reinstated in the Summer of 1942 at the request of the Armored Force to provide anti-aircraft protection for ground forces in the upcoming invasion of North Africa. The T28E1 was based on the M3 chassis unlike the original T28 which used the M2 chassis. Twin water cooled .50 caliber machine guns were used to acquire the target with tracer fire, at which time the 37MM cannon mounted under them would take the target under fire. (PAM)

The T28E1 mounted the cannon and machine gun arrangement on a rotating platform on a stripped M3 chassis. Due to the size of the gun mount the only extra room was just behind the cab where fuel and ammunition were stored. The gun crew either sat or stood on the mount to aim and fire the weapons. The round containers next to the gun and behind the cab are drums of .50 caliber machine gun ammunition. (PAM)

With the success of the T28 in North Africa the Army decided to resume production of the vehicle. Certain changes, however, were incorporated in the design based on field experience. The main change was the addition of a gun shield and .50 caliber air-cooled machine guns in place of the older water-cooled weapons used on the T28EI. Some thought was given to having a shield in front of the cannon and machine guns, but this was not used operationally since it limited forward visibility. (PAM)

(Below/Right) The gun shield did not cover the rear as it was felt that there was little to fear of hostile fire coming from this quarter. it also allowed more room for the crew to move about. (PAM)

The very simple box-like structure made the M15, which the vehicle was now designated, the most easily identifiable version of the M2/M3 series. Eventually 680 of these vehicles would be manufactured. (PAM)

The T28 was not originally fitted with any type of gun shield for protection of the gun crew. Later, there were several types of shields tried out on the vehicle but none ever went into production. These, however, laid the groundwork for the shield which was used on the M15 and M15A1 which replaced the T28. (PAM)

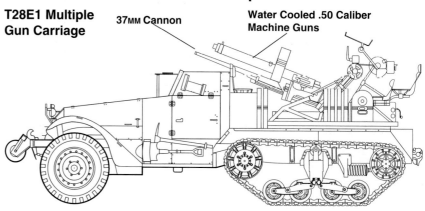

## T28/M15 Development

**T28E1 Multiple Gun Carriage**

37MM Cannon

Water Cooled .50 Caliber Machine Guns

The addition of the shield did make the M15 rather crowded and restricted movement, but the advantages of it for the crew more than compensated for this problem. Storage bin for 37MM ammunition were placed on the inside wall of the shied. (PAM)

Eventually the M15 was upgraded to the M15A1 version which featured a revised and improved fire control system, improvements in the M3 chassis to handle the additional weight, and the repositioning of the .50 caliber machine guns from above to below the 37MM cannon. The armored shield also had a folding flap added at the front which could be lowered to improve forward visibility. The M15A1 was the most common of the three variants built with over 1,600 coming off the production line between October of 1943 and February of 1944.

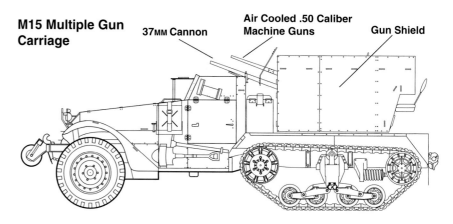

**M15 Multiple Gun Carriage**

Air Cooled .50 Caliber Machine Guns

37MM Cannon

Gun Shield

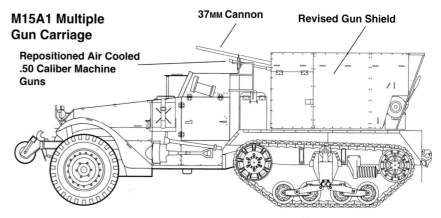

**M15A1 Multiple Gun Carriage**

37MM Cannon

Revised Gun Shield

Repositioned Air Cooled .50 Caliber Machine Guns

# M13/M16 Multiple Gun Motor Carriage

Concern over enemy air attacks on armored columns prompted work to begin during late 1940 on power-operated machine gun turrets. An M2 was fitted with a Bendix .50 caliber aircraft machine gun turret under the designation T1E1. This initial attempt proved unsuccessful, but in November of 1941, work began on two new prototypes using a turret, the M33, designed specifically by the W. L. Maxson Corporation for this purpose and a new aircraft turret being manufactured by the Martin Aircraft Company. Both turrets were mounted on the M2, the Maxson vehicle being designated T1E1, while the Martin turret vehicle was called the M1E3. Tests indicated that the M2 did not have enough room and that the M33 turret looked to be the more promising of the two. As a result, the M33 was mounted on an M3 under the designation T1E4.

The Maxson M33 consisted of a gun turret mounting two .50 caliber machine guns and a gasoline powered generator for gun elevation and turret traverse. A gunner sat in an open mount between the guns and provision was made for an armored shield to be mounted in front of him. Target acquisition was through a reflector sight and with the power generator, the turret could traverse 360 degrees in six seconds and the guns could go from -10 degrees to 90 degrees elevation in less than two seconds.

The two machine guns could fire bursts of 250 rounds per minute or 50 rounds per minute at a sustained rate of fire.

Tests with the T1E4 led to its acceptance during mid-1942 under the designation M13 Multiple Gun Motor Carriage (MGMC). As the M5 was also coming into service at this time the M33 was also mounted on it as the M14 MGMC.

While the M13/M14 was successful, the Army looked into ways to increase the weight of fire being thrown out. This led to the T61, which was an M2 which had a slightly modified Maxson mounted fitted with four .50 caliber machine guns. This unit proved so successful in tests that it was also accepted for production as the M45 and fitted, like the M33, to both the M3 and M5, under the designations M16 and M17 respectively.

An off-shoot of this program was the T10. This came about when the Army showed an interest in mounting the 20MM Oerlikeon anti-aircraft cannon used by the Navy on a modified Maxson turret. This modified turret was tested on both the M2 (T10) and M3 (T10E1). Eventually, 110 units were manufactured as the T10 MGMC on the M3 chassis, but problems with the 20MM cannon jamming under dusty condition led to all but one of the vehicles being rebuilt as M16s.

The M16 was the only version of the M3 series to be retained in any quantity as a first line weapon following the war. In fact, it was upgraded as the M16A1, which involved converting the standard M3s to the anti-aircraft role. Since the sides did not have the small folding panel on the rear sides, the Maxson turret was mounted on a higher pedestal for adequate clearance. During the Korean War, both the M16 and M16A1 had additional armored shields mounted alongside the turret to provide protection for the loaders from enemy small arms fire. These were the last M3 version used by the Army, surviving into the late 1960s with National Guard units, even seeing service during the Newark riots of 1967.

# T37 and T37E1

Unrelated to the M13/M16 project was the T37, which also investigated the possibility of mounting .50 caliber machine guns in a revolving mount. The T37 mounted four machine guns in a box pattern in a T60 mount. This was followed by the T37E1, which had the gun mounted in a line abreast with the middle two being slightly moved back. A circular shield of half inch armor was provided for crew protection. Test results were not encouraging and the project was dropped.

**The T1E2 utilized the same M2 chassis as the T1, with the rear side armor removed. The twin .50 caliber machine gun Maxson power turret was mounted on a pedestal in the middle of the rear compartment. With its own power operated generator this design, the T1E2 was able to function without the half-track engine running. The turret itself was designated the M33. (PAM)**

In 1940, a Bendix twin .50 caliber aircraft machine gun turret was fitted to a M2 half-track prototype under the designation T1, later being redesignated the T1E1. The attempt was not a success and was later revised with a new turret developed by the W. Maxson Corporation. The T1E1 arrangement was very cumbersome and had a high profile which, along with the technical aspects of the design, led to it s cancellation. (PAM)

The gunner sat in an open topped armored enclosure with the electrical generator and battery behind him. The .50 caliber air-cooled machine guns were fed from drums which could be quickly changed to keep up a high rate of fire.. The sight was located on the bar above the gunners seat. (PAM)

(Above/Left) Martin Aircraft had developed a new twin .50 caliber air cooled machine gun power turret intended for bomber aircraft. This turret was tested on an M2 chassis under the designation T1E3, but the Maxson turret M3 version showed more promise and the design was abandoned. (PAM)

The T1E4 eventually became the M13 on approval for production. Ammunition drums for the .50 caliber machine guns were carried either on a rack on the rear or in another rack behind the drivers compartment. Additional storage boxes were on either side of the ammunition cans. (PAM)

## M13 Multiple Gun
## Motor Carriage

M33 Twin .50 Caliber
Gun Turret

Folding
Section

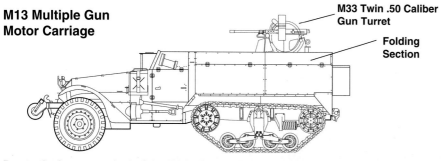

Due to the larger rear bed of the M3 half-track, it was decided to mount the Maxson gun turret on the M3 chassis under the designation T1E4. The armored sides of the M3 were retained, but the top portion was hinged and could be folded down in order to give the gun turret a greater field of fire. (PAM)

Since the M5 was also coming into service at this time for Lend-Lease use, it was also fitted with the Maxson turret under the designation M14. The shield for the gunner has not been fitted to the turret and the storage rack for the .50 caliber machine gun is visible behind the drivers position. The flat front fender and rounded rear corner were the main distinguishing points between the M13 and M14. (PAM)

The new gun turret differed very little from the original aside from the addition of two more .50 caliber machine guns. This turret was being demonstrated to senior Army officer during late 1942. (PAM)

Despite the success of the M13/M14, the Army felt there was a need for more firepower and this led to the four gun Maxson mount. This was tested on the chassis which had been used for the T1E2 prototype, under the designation T58. The revised turret was designated the M45 and the production version was designated M16. (PAM)

### M16 Multiple Gun Motor Carriage

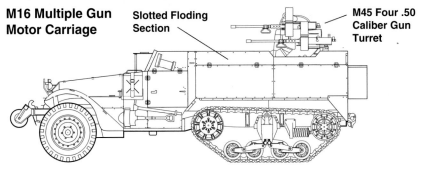

Slotted Floding Section

M45 Four .50 Caliber Gun Turret

Unlike the M13/14, the M16 had slots in the folding armor flap so that the lower machine guns could rotate without the sides being lowered. The Army was so pleased with the firepower of the M16 that over half the M13s were remanufactured as M16's. (PAM)

7

The cutouts in the side flaps were done to all three folding sides. With the power operated turret the gunner could traverse, elevate, or depress the the guns at sixty degrees per second. Lend-Lease models based on the M5 were designated the M17. (PAM)

The same configuration on the M3 was designated the T10E1. This model went into production as the T10 during early 1944, but problems with the cannons jamming under dusty conditions eventually led to all but one T10 being rebuilt as M16s. (PAM)

There was an interest in fitting 20ᴍᴍ canons to the Maxson mount which led to the T10 and T10E1. The T10 was the version tested on the M2, the T1E2 chassis again being utilized in the role. Basically the cannons replaced the machine guns. (PAM)

The M16 was one of the few versions of the M3 family which was kept in service following the Second World War. Used extensively during the Korean War, some were modified with additional shields to protect the crews from sniper fire. This "Bat Wing" armor was installed to the vehicle on the left, while the other vehicle is a standard M16. Both vehicles were assigned to the 82nd AAA Battalion of the 2nd Infantry Division in Korea during 1951. (PAM)

One of the more bizarre modification tried on a half-track chassis was the mounting of a Elco designed quad 20MM cannon and twin .50 caliber machine mount. This was nearly identical to the "Thunderbolt" mount used experimentally on a few PT boats. The turret threw out a tremendous weight of fire but never was envisioned for actual use in the field. (PAM)

The T37 and T37E1 were another attempt to mount a battery of 20MM cannon in a revolving turret. The main difference between the two were the gun arrangement. In the T37 the four guns were mounted in a square pattern while the T37E1 had them in a staggered line abreast. This vehicle was the T37E1 prototype. (PAM)

The four 20MM cannons were mounted in a staggered row with two .50 caliber sighting machine guns above. This chassis was the same chassis used to test the T28 prototype. (PAM)

The gun arrangement appears to be rather complex and the close confines of the turret area must have made servicing the guns awkward to say the least. The turret itself was composed of half inch armor. (PAM)

# 40mm Gun Motor Carriage

The success of the T28/M15 series prompted efforts to mount a 40mm cannon on the M3, as it was felt that the heavier hitting power and range of the 40mm gun would be an improvement over the 37mm cannon. Unfortunately, all official attempts to come up with such a conversion were unsuccessful, although four different prototypes were tested.

## T54 and T54E1

The first development began in June of 1942, when an M3 was fitted with an M1 40mm anti-aircraft gun. Designated T54, the arrangement proved to be unstable when fired, which affected accuracy. As a result, modifications were made to the design and a second vehicle, designated the T54E1, was completed. Stability problems still existed and it was decided to

**In mid-1942 work began on a development of the M3 fitted with a 40mm cannon. The first model was the T94 which had a 40mm Bofors mount fitted directly behind the drivers compartment. The gas tank was moved to a position below and behind the gun mount. This first attempt met with failure as the recoil from the gun and the weight of it overstressed the M3 chassis. (PAM)**

revise the original design. The T54E1 also featured a shield like turret and additional stowage.

## T59 and T59E1

The stability problems with the T54E1 led to the decision to incorporate outriggers to provide a steady platform for the 40mm gun. The basic revision of the T54E1 resulted in the T59. A further development of this was the T59E1, which had a T17 Fire Control System.

## T60 and T60E1

Based on the experiences with the T54 and T59 vehicles, the T60 was a combination of tests with them. An addition to the basic design was two .50 caliber machine guns mounted similar to the M15/M15A1 arrangement. This combination mount was designated the T65. Modifications of the design, including shields and revised stowage, resulted in the T59E1.

# T68

Of all the attempts to mount a 40MM cannon on the M3, the T68 was the most bizarre. Two guns were mounted above each other with overhead equilibratiors for balance. The basic body outline was also modified and the fenders and running boards were removed.

# 40MM GMC (Field Modification)

This vehicle was a very unique variant of the M3 series as it never received an official designation. Referred to as the M15 Special or 40MM GMC (Expedient Mount) in various articles it came about as the result of modifications made by the Cooper Plains 99th Ordnance Depot in Australia. In all probability, M3s were used for the conversion, although M13s may have also been used. It appears unlikely that the M15 version was used, although originally this version was thought to have been the basis for the modification and the early unofficial designation of M15 Special.

The depot modified an unspecified number of vehicles to carry a 40MM gun in an eight sided revolving turret arrangement. One gas tank was moved forward behind the drivers compartment where a bulkhead was added. A large storage box was added to the rear for ammunition, while two additional boxes were on either side of the fuel tank. Since the vehicle was intended from the beginning as a ground support vehicle, rather than for use in the anti-aircraft role, the stability problem was not a critical factor and was probably why the vehicle was placed into service in the Philippines with the 209th AAA Battalion.

**The T54E1 was a modification of the T54 idea with outriggers added for stabilization. In addition a revolving turret was added for crew protection along with additional storage and overhead cover for the drivers compartment. This design was rejected for most of the same reasons as the T54. (PAM)**

**The T59 and T59E1 were an attempt to correct the problems with the T54 design. Outriggers were tried but again proved unsuccessful in solving the gun platform stability problem. This T59E1 carried a revised fire control system. (PAM)**

**The data from the T54 and T59 tests led to the T60 which used a combination of jacks and outriggers for stabilization. With revised storage and shields this became the T60E1. The 40MM cannon had twin .50 caliber machine guns mounted under it as with the M15A1. While the jacks and outriggers helped, the project was still not deemed a satisfactory solution to the problem and was canceled. (PAM)**

The T68 featured twin 40mm cannons mounted one above the other with an overhead equalizer. There was only one prototype produced before the design was cancelled. (PAM)

(Below and Right) While nothing came of the various official attempts to mount a 40mm gun in the M3, in Australia the 99th Ordnance Depot converted a number of half-tracks to carry 40mm guns. Basically the cannon was mounted in a revolving box-like turret with additional ammunition storage in a large box on the rear. (PAM)

# Combat Operations

The first use of the M2/M3 series in combat was in the Philippine Islands following the Japanese initiation of hostilities in December of 1941. Prior to the attack on Pearl Harbor, strenuous efforts had been made to reinforce American forces in the islands. These reinforcements included both M2s and M3s, which were used by the 192nd and 194th Tank Battalions, each of which received twenty-three vehicles. These were used for reconnaissance duties with headquarters units. In addition, fifty M3 75MM GMCs were also sent and used to equip the Provisional Field Artillery Brigade. Included among these M3s were some of the early T12s.

While the M2s and M3s made no outstanding contribution to the defense of Luzon, the M3 75MM GMCs were used extensively in support of armor and ground troops in the direct fire support role and against Japanese armor. Radio reports detailing the activities of the vehicles helped highlight their weak and strong points and were of some help in improving the vehicles and refining tactics. Some vehicles were captured when the Philippines fell and were used against U.S. forces when they returned to the islands in 1944, with little impact.

The next major use of the vehicle in combat came with the invasion of North Africa in November of 1942. During this campaign, both the M2 and M3 were used, along with the M3 75MM GMC, T28, T30 and T19. Unfortunately, armored doctrine at the time was still in its infancy and many mistakes were made. Shortcomings, due in part to poor tactics, were also uncovered. In particular, the M2 and M3 were singled out for their lack of overhead protection and the inability of their armor to stop heavy machine gun fire. The improper employment of the M3 75MM GMC also resulted in heavy losses. Rather then being used in the intended ambush role, they were used in a more aggressive, forward manner where their thin armor led to heavy losses against German tanks.

There were, however, some bright sides to the overall picture. When used in the proper role, the M3 75MM GMCs did achieve some noteworthy results, particularly at the Battle of El Guettar in March of 1943. The T28s were very effective in the anti-aircraft role, destroying large numbers of German aircraft. And, in their intended role as personnel carriers, the M3s did a creditable job in keeping pace with the tanks of the armored units, and with their machine guns, provided much needed support when the infantry dismounted to attack.

In the Pacific, there was little need for large numbers of M2s and M3s due to the terrain. The main variant employed initially after the Philippines was the M3 75MM GMC, which was used extensively by the Marines in their Special Weapons Companies, assigned to each division. These were used primarily in the direct fire support role since rarely were Japanese tanks encountered. Eventually, when American forces invaded the Philippines during 1944, more use was made of the M3, including the M13, M16 and converted M3s fitted with 40MM cannons. In general, however, the M2/M3 series was not used in large numbers in comparison to the European Theater.

Following North Africa the Allies invaded Sicily and Italy. Again the various versions of the half-track were committed to action, but for the earlier special purpose types, such as the M3 75MM GMC, T30 and T19, their use was fast coming to an end. Newer armored vehicles like the M10 Tank Destroyer, M7 Priest and M8 75MM HMC were replacing them and the remaining vehicles were relegated to training or given to the British or French. In particular, the M3 75MM GMC saw extensive service with British forces in Italy as self-propelled artillery, rather than as a tank destroyer. The terrain in Sicily and Italy, however, was not conducive to large scale mobile armored warfare and as a result, the M2/M3 was not used as was intended in general, but rather in a support role.

The largest employment of the half-track came during the campaign in Western Europe following the invasion of Normandy and Southern France. By this time, the doctrine of armored infantry had been refined through trial and experience under combat conditions. Since the armored infantry was assigned to armored divisions, whose role was considered offensive, the armored infantry were literally at the spearhead of the attack once the Allies broke out of the Normandy beachhead in the late Summer of 1944. Following the rupture of the German lines, the various Allied armored divisions raced across France trying to cut off the German retreat. The half-tracks allowed the infantry to keep pace with the tanks over uneven ground, and gave much needed mobility to the troops which was often lacking in the regular infantry units. While the infantry did not usually attack while mounted, the half-tracks could provide a base of fire with their machine guns and it was not unusual to see M3s festooned with three or more guns which had been scrounged or requisitioned to supplement their standard armament.

Due to their mobility, the armored infantry often saw a great deal more combat than their

**While the first use of half-tracks in combat took place in the Philippines during late 1941 and early 1942, it was not until the invasion of North Africa that they were used by American forces on a large scale. Initially they saw little combat as French forces quickly came over to the Allied cause. These T19s, fitted with shields, take part in a part in Rabat French Morocco in December of 1942. (Army)**

infantry counter-parts. When there arose the need for quick reaction to a German counter-attack, tanks and armored infantry were often rushed into the breach.

In the drive across Europe, aside from the M2 and M3, the other variants to see significant action were the mortar carriers and anti-aircraft variants. In particular, the M15/M15A1, and the M16 proved very useful in a role not originally intended. Due to the overwhelming Allied air superiority, the Luftwaffe played a negligible role in the ground war. As a result, the anti-aircraft units often provided fire support to ground units. The M16s proved especially effective in this role, earning the nickname, "meat-choppers" since the high rate of fire of their four .50 caliber machine guns would literally tear attacking infantry to piece if caught out in the open.

By the time hostilities came to a close in Europe, the various armored units had become a fine well honed fighting machine. In no small part this was due to the excellent cooperation between the tanks and armored infantry in their half-tracks. To lesser degrees, other allied armored units used half-tracks in conjunction with their tanks, but by comparison their usage never approached that which the U.S. Army achieved.

# Post-War

With the end of the Second World War, the Army began to downsize and evaluate the lessons learned from the conflict. The half-track came under close scrutiny and many of its failings came to light under the quieter conditions of peace.

During the war, the Army had introduced the M39, a tracked personnel carrier based on the M18 Hellcat tank destroyer. In light of the limitations of the half-tracked vehicles, the Army decided to work on fully tracked armored personnel carriers (APCs) rather than pursue the

This M2 half-track has been fitted with a 37mm anti-tank gun taken from a Dodge 3/4 ton truck which had been intended for use as a tank destroyer under the designation M6 37mm GMC. This weapon proved totally inadequate in this role and, in this case, it was mounted on the M2 to provide better protection and mobility. This vehicle was from the 601st Tank Destroyer Battalion, 1st Armored Division based in Oran, French Morocco. The U.S. star is on a Blue circle, The Y is Red on a Yellow square with a small II in the lower left corner. (PAM)

half-track configuration. This led to the M44, M59 and eventually to the M113 APCs which became the standard carried for the Army for nearly three decades until replaced by the M2/M3 Bradley. Whether by coincidence or design, this vehicle came in two distinct versions and used the designation M2 and M3, just like its ancestors had done forty years earlier.

While the M2 quickly disappeared, the M3s continued to soldier on, but the M16 was one version which the Army decided to keep in the inventory and even update. When the Korean War broke out in June of 1950, U.S. troops in Japan were rushed to stem the North Korean onslaught. They brought with them M3s, M15A1s, M16s and M3 40mm GMCs. Later, additional vehicles were brought to Korea with additional U.S. formations, but by the end of the war, only the M16 was being used in large numbers. As in the Second World War, it and the other anti-aircraft vehicles were used primarily in the support role, with the M16 being particularly effective with its machine guns against Chinese "human wave" attacks or against enemy positions. This, however, was the swan song of the M3 series in U.S. service, since after the war, the remaining half-tracks were either sold as scrap, used as targets, or given to U.S. allies. Some were salvaged by civilian contractors, stripped of their armor and used in the construction and logging businesses and occasionally may still be seen in these roles.

Other U.S. allies received large numbers of surplus vehicles under the Military Aid Program (MAP) following the Second World War. These vehicles were used in many of the lesser known conflicts which have plagued the world since 1945, but the two most notable were probably the French in Indochina and Israel in the Middle East.

As U.S. forces pushed east they began to come into contact with seasoned German forces and quickly realized that they had a lot to learn. The crew of this M3 75mm Gun Motor Carriage has camouflaged their vehicle with mud to help it blend in better with the surrounding terrain. The initial use of the M3 75mm GMC as a tank destroyer showed how U.S. tactics needed to be changed in light of actual combat experience which, unfortunately, was often learned in defeat at the hands of the battle hardened German troops. (PAM)

The light armor of the M2 and M3 was not sufficient to stop anything heavier than small arms fire, a lesson which was learned the hard way in North Africa. This T19 was destroyed by artillery fire at Sened, Tunisia. Gradually it was realized that the lightly armored half-tracks and gun mounts could not be expected to slug it out with German forces from exposed conditions and tactics were rethought to better use the vehicles and curtail losses. Eventually, most of the gun motor carriages were replaced with better suited vehicles which were designed expressly for their specialized roles. ( Army)

When France reoccupied Indochina after the Second World War, it became involved in a vicious guerrilla war with the communist Viet Minh under Ho Chi Minh and Nguyen Giap. The initial French forces included M2s, M3s, M5s and M9s, along with light tanks and armored cars. Initially the French were able to make quick strikes to secure population centers and roads, but as the war progressed, the Viet Minh resorted to classic guerrilla warfare, only attacking when they were assured of surprise and overwhelming strength. Convoys were prime targets and the French were soon hard pressed to keep pace with the enemy. As the war progressed, additional half-tracks were supplied by the U.S., especially after the start of the Korean War. In early 1951, with the arrival of General Lattre de Tassigny, French forces were reorganized to deal more effectively with the Viet Minh. Half-tracks were combined with M24 Chaffe light tanks in armored groups called "Groupment Blinders" (GB's) for offensive use. While these units initially enjoyed some success, they were basically road bound  which limited their radius of action and allowed the Viet Minh to set up elaborate ambushes, further extracting a terrible toll of French men and material. After the fall of Dien Bein Phu in May of 1954, a cease fire was arranged and the country was partitioned into North and South Vietnam. The new South Vietnamese Army received some of the half-tracks which were used until newer American equipment, like the M113 APC became available in the 1960s. While there has been some contention that U.S. forces also used M3 variants when they first arrived in Vietnam during the mid-1960s, no hard evidence has yet surfaced to confirm this, which seems unlikely to have occurred.

Without a doubt, the largest post war usage of the half-track series was by the Israeli Defense Force (IDF). During the initial fight for Israel in 1948, half-tracks were one type of armor available to the Israelis to defend their new land. These were smuggled into the country and fitted with a wide variety of weapons. Almost every type of half-track which was around at the end of the war was acquired by the IDF in its quest for arms, and by 1950, well

over 200 half-tracks were in service. Eventually, the Israelis began to standardize these by using the same engine and folding the right side of the drivers armor plate down and fitting it with a ball mounted machine gun. In addition, on M2 and M4 models, rear doors were added to lessen troop exposure to enemy fire when exiting the vehicle. Following the 1956 Suez Campaign, more half-tracks were obtained and these were added to the IDFs growing fleet. Aside from infantry carriers, they were fitted with anti-tank guns (90MM) and missiles (SS11s) for use as tank destroyers, mortar carriers mounting 120MM mortars, and with a variety of guns for anti-aircraft defense. One of the most effective of these was the mating of twin 20MM cannons to a modified Maxson turret similar to the M13/M16 configuration. These were used quite effectively in the 1973 Yom Kippur War, and continued to soldier on with reserve units after being replaced by the M163 Vulcan.

The IDF use of the M3 half-track series was perhaps the most unique of the vehicle's history and could fill a book in its own right. From its early use in 1948 when anything from 20MM cannons to 2 pounders in turrets, or 6 pounders with their wheels removed were mounted on half-tracks to the missile armed tank destroyers, the Israelis use of the M3 has been one of ingenuity and resourcefulness. Even when newer vehicles like the M113 became available after the Six Day War in 1967, many Israel officers and soldiers preferred the open toped half-tracks to the more confined APCs. Although eventually, the M113 won out, the M3 continued to be used by reserve forces and as special purpose mounts for engineers, medical units, communications and anti-aircraft forces. While its days as a front-line AFV have disappeared, it is likely that the M3 will serve in the IDF in one role or another into the next century.

The green American troops suffered a number of humiliating defeats at the hands of the Germans initially loosing large quantities of supplies and equipment. This half-track variant has been refitted with a cannon and repainted and marked prominently with a German cross to  avoid be fired on mistakenly by German forces. The camouflage scheme is probably U.S. Olive Drab and German Sand.

An M2 towing a 57MM anti-tank gun passes through a French town during Operation COBRA in July of 1944. One of the keys to the success of the American and Allied drive was the ability of the infantry to keep up with the hard driving tankers and provide the much needed support the armored force required. This denied the Germans the time and ability to reform and regroup after the Allied breakout from the Normandy beachhead. (PAM)

As in North Africa, the Germans still made use of captured equipment to supplement their own resources, although there was far less U.S. equipment captured now that the U.S. troops had some combat experience under their belt. This German crew have camouflaged their vehicle with vegetation to gain some measure of cover from the ever present Allied fighters which ruled the skies over France in the Summer of 1944.

An M2 from the 645th Tank Destroyer Battalion lies knocked out along with an M4 Sherman medium tank just down the road. While there is no obvious battle damage it appears that the vehicle has been stripped of personal gear, probably by enemy troops. Despite the lessons learned in North Africa the practice of marking vehicles with prominent White stars, which provided convenient aiming points for German gunners, was still being done by some units and commanders.

One interesting conversion was this M3 which has been fitted with a loudspeaker to induce enemy troops to surrender. The soldier to the right is speaking into the microphone in an attempt to get the German troops to give up. (PAM)

When the Germans launched their final attack of the war against Allied forces in the Battle of the Bulge, American troops were forced to fight over long distances under very inclement weather conditions. This M2A1 has been given a coat of lime Whitewash to help it blend in with the snowy conditions which became very severe after the initial German assault in mid-December of 1945. The mechanized infantry were used extensively as their half-tracks gave them the needed mobility to counter the German attack in conjunction with their armored counterparts. (PAM)

An M3A1 drives through the streets of Anrochte, Germany with the town crier aboard, who reads the new rules of military occupation to the civilian residents. Despite its relatively peaceful mission the crew are on the lookout for any signs of resistance from diehard Nazis. (PAM)

During the Battle of the Bulge, Luftwaffe fighters made an appearance over the battlefield which was very uncommon due to Allied air superiority. This M15A1 guards a bridge in Limbourg, Belgium in late December of 1944. It is from Battery D of the 197th Anti-Aircraft Artillery Battalion.

Probably the most effective M3 variant was the M16, which was used with outstanding success against massed Chinese and Korean infantry attacks and enemy bunkers and trench lines. The concentrated fire power of the four .50 caliber machine guns was awesome and could decimate a ground attack force or wipe out an enemy position. This M16 is being used to support an attack on Hill 860. (Army)

When the Korean War broke out U.S. Army units in Japan were rushed to the scene. Despite the fact that the M3 and most of its variants were no longer considered first line equipment, many units still were using them. This M15A1 moves up along the Kum River in July of 1950. After the commitment of U.S. airpower there was little threat from North Korean air attacks and most anti-aircraft units were used mainly in the ground support role. (Army)

This M16 has been fitted with extra shields around the gun mount to provide additional protection for the loaders. Because of their heavy firepower these vehicles were often targeted by the communists in an attempt to knock them out. In particular, the crews, especially the loaders, were inviting targets for snipers. (PAM)

This M15A1 was part of the Turkish Brigade which was attached the U.S. 25th Infantry Division. It appears that the name on the side of the turret is "Ankara". (PAM)

Aside from the Korean War the M3 took part in a number of other conflict throughout the world. In Indochina, the French Union Forces employed them in a wide variety of roles. This M3 from the 4e Escadron, 1e Regiment Etraner de Cavalerie, of the French Foreign Legion has been fitted with a metal frame to which a canvas cover has been added, both to keep out the hot sun and to act as a grenade shield. A small gun shield has been mounted above the drivers compartment. The PSP on the side could be used to help extract the vehicle from the mud but also doubles as additional protection. (ECPA)

As part of military aid packages the U.S. supplied numerous allies with surplus American equipment in the 1950s and 1960s. This M3 of the Venezuelan Army tows a 40MM Bofors cannon during a parade. The roundel on the side is, from the inside out, Red, Blue and Yellow. (PAM)

When the French left Indochina they turned some of their equipment over to the fledgling South Vietnamese Army. This M3A1 was found abandoned by the author near Tan Son Nhut Air Base in the Spring of 1972, rusting in a small ARVN armor compound, much the worse for wear. (Mesko)

The largest post Second World War user of the M3 series was the Israeli Defense Force (IDF), which began acquiring half-tracks during 1948. This M5, from the 82nd Tank Battalion, leads a mechanized column in the Negev desert during December of 1948. (IDF)

A number of M3s were converted to carry French SS-11 anti-tank missiles. These did not prove to be successful and the missiles were dropped from the IDF inventory and the M3s were converted to other uses. The basic modification aside from the missiles and their related systems were the addition of a roof over the drivers and rear compartment. (IDF)

The IDF modified the Maxson mount to hold two 20mm cannons, with the designation TCM-20. Unlike the M16 variant this version did not have folding sides. Ammunition was supplied to the cannons in sixty round drums. (IDF)

Following the 1965 Six Day War there was a move to re-equip IDF units with more modern M113 APCs. Although regular mechanized units had received these, reserve units were still equipped with the M3 and used them extensively during the Yom Kippur War in 1973. This heavily laden M3 moves up toward the Suez front after the initial Egyptian breakthrough. The added machine gun mount next to the drivers position was standard for IDF M3s used in mechanized units. (IDF)

This IDF M3 has been fitted with a single 20mm cannon, which although designed for use against aircraft also proved effective against ground targets. It also proved effective against Syrian helicopters which tried to use anti-tank missiles against Israeli armor in Lebanon. The jerrycan rack along the engine compartment has been modified to hold two cans. (IDF)